The huge suc of *Rugby Songs* has led many ardent rugby players and poetry lovers to complain that a number of their particular favourites were left out. *More Rugby Songs* more than makes up for the omissions. Collected here for the first time are more than a hundred songs from *When I Was Only Seventeen* to *The Mayor of Bayswater's Daughter*.

More
Rugby Songs

SPHERE BOOKS LIMITED
London and Sydney

First published in Great Britain by Sphere Books Ltd 1968
30–32 Gray's Inn Road, London WC1X 8JL
This collection copyright © Harry Morgan 1968
Reprinted 1968 (twice), 1969, 1970, 1971, 1973, 1976,
1978, 1979, 1981, 1984, 1985

PUBLISHERS' NOTE
The Publishers acknowledge that some of the items in this volume may bear a
relationship, however denatured to other poems or stories actually written by poets
intent on purposes other than conviviality. There may even be some of those authors
who, not being rugby fans, consider that the present version of their work deserves,
if not suppression, some acknowledgement to its original creator. In the absence of
such credit, which might in too many cases have justifiably annoyed the originator
from whose work the script here included was derived, the Publishers apologise to the
poets. If any of you who can prove ownership wish credit in the form of cash and
are prepared to come forward, at whatever risk to reputation or good name, the
Publishers are prepared to negotiate a reasonable settlement – quietly, and out
of court.

TRADE
MARK

Set in Intertype Baskerville

Printed and bound in Great Britain by
Collins, Glasgow

MORE RUGBY SONGS

MORE RUGBY SONGS

List of Contents

PSALM

We were walking down the street: we saw a
house: it was on fire.
There was a man standing on the roof
shouting: Help, I am on fire.
We shouted: Jump.
Jump, you silly ******* bugger, for we have
a blanket.
He jumped,
He fell,
He hit the deck,
He broke his neck.
For we had no blanket.
We laughed. My God, how we laughed.
We laughed until the tears ran down our
trouser legs.
The next day we buried him.
For he was dead.
****holes.

PLEASE DON'T BURN OUR ****HOUSE DOWN

*Please don't burn our ****house down,*
Mother is willing to pay,
Father's sailing the high seas
And Joan's in the family way.

My brother has got gonorrhoea,
*Don't make us **** in the rain,*
Little Jim has got the runs
And he wants to go there again.

*Please don't burn our ****house down,*
*For times are ******* hard,*
And if you burn the old thing down,
*We'll have to **** in the yard.*

IN FAR GLAMORGAN

*There was a young fellow whose name was
Dick
Who had, poor fellow, a corkscrew *****
He spent his time in a lifelong hunt
To find a girl with a spiral ****.*

*He finished his search in far Glamorgan
When he found a girl with such an organ
But on his wedding night he fell down dead
'Cause he found the girl had a left hand
thread.*

FARTING CONTEST

I'll tell you a tale that is sure to please
Of a grand farting contest at Shitton-on-Pease
*Where all the best ***** parade in the fields*
To compete in the contest for various shields.

*Some tighten their ***** and fart up the scale*
To compete for a cup and a barrel of ale
*While others whose ***** are biggest and strongest*
Compete in the section for loudest and longest.

Now this year's events had drawn a big crowd
And the betting was even on Mrs McLeod
For it had appeared in the evening edition
*That this lady's **** was in perfect condition.*

Now old Mrs Jones had a perfect backside
Half a forest of hairs with a wart on each side
And she fancied her chance of winning with ease
Having trained on a diet of cabbage and peas.

The Vicar arrived and ascended the stand
And thus he addressed this remarkable band
"The contest is on as is shown on the bills
We've precluded the use of injections and pills."

Mrs Bindle arrived amid roars of applause
And promptly proceeded to pull down her drawers
Fo tho' she'd no chance in the farting display
She'd the prettiest **** you'd seen in a day.

Now young Mrs Pothole was backed for a place
Though she'd often been placed in the deepest disgrace
By dropping a fart that had beaten the organ
And the poor Vicar, Old Jonathan Morgan.

The ladies lined up, the signal to start
And winning the toss Mrs Jones took first fart
The people around stood in silence and wonder
While the wireless announced gale warnings and thunder.

Now Mrs Mcleod reckoned nothing of this
She'd had some weak tea and was all wind and ****
So she took up her place with her **** opened wide
But unluckily **** and was disqualified

Then young Mrs Pothole was called to the front
And started by doing a wonderful stunt
She took a deep breath and clenching her hands
She blew the whole roof off the popular stands.

That left Mrs Bindle who shyly appeared
And smiled at the clergy who lustily cheered
And though it was reckoned her chances were small
She ran out a winner, outfarting them all.

With hands on her hips she stood farting alone,
And the crowd stood amazed at the sweetness of tone
And the clergy agreed without hindrance or pause
And said, "First to Mrs Bindle, Now pull up your drawers."

But with muscles well tensed and legs full apart
She started a final and glorious fart
Beginning with Chopin and ending with Wing
She went right up the scale to God Save the King.

She went to the rostrum with maidenly gait
And took from the Vicar a set of gold plate
Then she turned to the Vicar with sweetness sublime
And smilingly said "Come and see me some time."

ANTI WAR PANACEA

If the Polish financier Koc
Met the Czechoslovakian Kundt
It would strengthen the Latvian bloc
It would stiffen the Popular Front.

Uniting the part with the whole
How fertile the issue would be
For the Czech would lie down with the Pole
And Berlin be, of course, on the spree.

The Marital powers would achieve
With naval disarmament peace;
Which wouldn't be hard to conceive
From the seamen this act would release.

And the press, of the Chamberlain school
Would score a political hit
With headlines of "Communist Tool
Widens Czechoslovakian split."

It would strengthen the Latvian bloc
It would stiffen the Popular Front
If the Polish financier Koc
Met the Czechoslovakian Kundt.

ABYSSINIA

*Il Duce gives the order to march against the
foe
And off to Abyssynia the Organ Grinders go
But now they are incapable of any sort of
grind
For they're back from Abyssinia with their
organs left behind.*

*The hosts of Abyssinians return to hearth and
home
With knick-knacks for the mantelpiece
imported straight from Rome.
The Pope is inundated with prayers to join his
choir
From men whose normal voices are now an
octave higher.*

*Il Duce mounts the rostrum as regiments
return
With the Unknown Eunuch's ashes in a truly
Roman urn.
For some great gift of gratitude this state
occasion calls
"What shall we give our heroes?"—and the
heroes answer "BALLS".*

ODE TO THE FOUR LETTER WORDS

Banish the use of the four-letter words
Whose meanings are never obscure
The Anglos, the Saxons those hardy old birds,
Were vulgar, obscene and impure.
But cherish the use of the weasling phrase
That never quite says what you mean
You'd better be known for your hypocrite
ways
Than as vulgar, obscene and impure.

When Nature is calling, plain speaking is out,
When the Ladies, God bless 'em are milling
about;
You may pee-wee, make water or empty the
glass
You can powder you nose, even Johnny can
pass.
Shake the dew off the lily, see a man about a
dog;
When everyone's soused, it's condensing the
fog;
But please to remember, if you would know
bliss
That only in Shakespeare do characters ****.

A woman has bosoms, a bust or a breast
Those lily-white swellings that bulge 'neath
her vest

They are towers of ivory or sheaves of new
wheat
In a moment of passion ripe apples to eat.
You may speak of her nipples as fingers of fire
With hardly a question of raising her ire;
But by Rabbelais' beard, she will throw several
fits
If you speak of them roundly as good, honest
tits.

It's a cavern of joy you're thinking of now,
A warm tender field awaiting the plough;
It's a quivering pigeon caressing your hand,
Or the National Anthem—it makes us all
stand.
It's known amongst men as the centre of love
The hope of the world or a velvety glove.
But friend, heed this warning, beware the
afront,
Of aping the Saxon—don't call it a ****.

Though a lady repel your advance, she'll be
kind
As long as you intimate what's on your mind;
You may tell her you're hungry, you need to
be swung,
You may ask her to see how your etchings are
hung.
Or mention the ashes that need to be hauled;
Put the lid on her saucepan, even 'lay' is not
too bald;

But the moment you're forthright, get ready to duck,
For the girl isn't born yet who'll stand for
"Let's ****."

So banish the words that Elizabeth used,
When she was a Queen on her throne;
The modern maid's virtue is easily bruised
By the four-letter words all alone.
Let your morals be clean as an Alderman's vest
If your language is always obscure
Today not the act but the word is the test
Of the vulgar, obscene and impure.

TRYING

He tried me on the sofa
He tried me on the chair
He tried me on the window-sill
But he couldn't get it there.
He tried me on the verandah
I stood against the wall
I even sat upon the floor
But it would not act at all.
He worked it back and forwards
He tried both front and rear
But it was all too useless
His thing was out of gear.
He tried it this and that way
And oh, how I did laugh
To see how many ways he tried
To take my photograph . . . .

HOW MUCH TO OLDHAM?

In Market Street, Manchester, one summer night,
There was only one cab on the rank,
The driver was reading the "News of the World",
And quietly enjoying a wank.
He was dreaming that Venus, was kissing his
*****
The shaking was making him tired,
When a waitress named Lena, with tits like Sabrina
Came over and gently enquired.

"How much will you charge me to Oldham?"
The cab driver nearly dropped dead.
He got such a shock, he let go of his ****
and "Barclayed" his gear knob instead.
He said, "That's all right, I'm not busy tonight,
You're a nice sort of girl, I can tell,
So I won't charge you nothing to 'old em
If you'll let me 'old yours as well!"
                    ********* Hell!*)*
If you'll let me 'old yours as well!"

IN THE VIOLET TIME

*Violate me in the violet time, in the vilest way
you know,
Ruin me, ravage me, brutally savage me,
On me, no mercy show.
Don't give me a man who is selfish and
treacherous,
I want a man who is generous and lecherous,
Violate me in the violet time, in the vilest way
you know.*

THE CHILD THAT I CARRY

The child that I carry will have to be
Left on the steps of a nunnery,
The boy I called my own,
Puts on roll-ons and stockings, and smells of
Cologne.
His toenails are polished, he dyes his hair,
He's known on The Dilly as Zena Dare,
'Stead of flittin', he sits knittin',
For a policeman he met in Thames Ditton,
I must wed another, 'cos he loves my brother,
not me.

Uncle Dick and Auntie Mable
Fainted at the breakfast table.
This should be a solemn warning
Not to do it in the morning.

Uncle Ned has much improved
Since he had his balls removed.
Not only has he lost desire
He now sings treble in the choir.

At a party little Dick
Shouted "Someone suck my *****."
Women fainted, strong men shuddered.
Father said "Well, I'll be buggered."

Little Francis, home from school
Picked up baby by the tool
Nursie said "Now Master Francis
Don't spoil baby's ******* chances."

Little Miss Muffet sat on a tuffet
Her knickers all tattered and torn
It wasn't a spider that sat down beside her
But Little Boy Blue with his horn.

IF

If you can keep your girl when all about you
Are losing theirs and blaming it on you;
And keep the faith of wives though husbands
doubt you
And yet keep out of the Divorce Courts too —

If you can meet a girl and take her virtue
Before you've had the time to learn her
name —
And say to virgins "This is going to hurt you"
And yet go on and do it just the same.

If you don't hesitate when she says "Maybe"
And lead her on with every sort of lie;
And when she says she's going to have a baby
Just quickly raise your hat and say
good-bye —

If you can meet a new girl every minute
And not be faithful to a single one
Yours is the world and every woman in it
And, what is more, you'll be a cad, my son.

WHEN I WAS ONLY SEVENTEEN

When I was only seventeen
I found I had a ****
And if I struggled very hard
I could get my finger in
But now that I am twenty-four
My **** has lost its charm
And I can get my finger in
And half my ******* arm.

THE GAY CABALERO

There once was a gay Cabalero
Who lived in Rio de Janeiro
And call his John Thomas—Miralto Maree
Miralto, Miralto, Miralto Maree.

He went to a low down thee-atre
An exceedingly low down thee-atre
And of course he took with him Miralto
Maree
Miralto, Miralto, Miralto Maree.

He saw there a fair senhorita
And he made an appointment to meet her
To introduce her to Miralto Maree
His old friend Miralto, Miralto Maree

He showed her bull fights in the Corso
And she gazed at the Picador's torso
Which lowered the lance of Miralto Maree
Miralto, Miralto, Miralto Maree.

He took her to dine at a Casa
And filled her with Vino-de-Gaza
And then he suggested Miralto Maree
His old friend, Miralto Maree.

He took her upstairs to a room-a
And he ripped off her crepe-de-chine bloomer
And he showed her his old friend Miralto
Maree
Miralto, Miralto, Miralto Maree.

She lay on a comfy four-poster
And the cavalier bounded across her
And then he inserted Miralto Maree
Miralto, Miralto, Miralto Maree.

But she was a whore from the street-a
And she gave him a roaring clapeta
Which blackened the end of Miralto Maree
Miralto, Miralto, Miralto Maree.

Next week he had an inspection
An exceedingly thorough inspection
There were spots on the end of Miralto Maree
Miralto, Miralto, Miralto Maree.

So he went to a Physiciana
Who lopped off his massive banana
And said "You must part with Miralto Maree
Your old friend Miralto, Miralto Maree."

So now he's just got a stumpeta
And he finds it damn hard to pumpita
He can hardly get hold of Miralto Maree
Miralto, Miralto, Miralto Maree.

And the girls in Rio de Janeiro
They give him a jolly good jeer-o
For what can he do with Miralto Maree
Miralto, Miralto, Miralto Maree.

And the moral of this small sonita
Is don't **** a girl when you meet her
But cover the end of Miralto Maree
Your old pal Miralto, Miralto Maree.

And now that my story is ended
I hope you will not be offended
If you are, you can **** what is left of Maree
Miralto, Miralto, Miralto Maree.

LITTLE SISTER LILY

Have you met my Uncle Hector
He's a cock and ball inspector
At a celebrated public school.
And my brother sells french letters
And a patent cure for wetters
We're not the best of families,
  Ain't it crool.

Little sister Lily is a whore in Piccadilly
Mother is a strumpet on the Strand
*While Father hawks his ****hole*
At the Elephant and Castle
*We are a ******* family*
  Ain't it grand.

*There's a dirty, stinking piss house to the
north of Waterloo,
There's another one for ladies further down
That is kept by Sally Tucker, for a shilling you
can **** her,
You can sleep with her for only half a crown.*

*Though she's known as Sally Tucker by those
who used to **** her
Her real name is Talullah Johnstone Black
She has handled many a tool from the days
she first left school
And has earned a damn fine living on her
back.*

*She's the dirtiest of bitches, by the colour of
her britches,
You would think that dame had never had a
wash.
Yet the smell from her vagina is infinitely finer
Than any whisky, gin or rum and lemon
squash.*

*One night she had a rattle by a sailor from
Seattle
And she wondered why he hugged her so long
and close
When he finished with his screwing, she knew
what he'd been doing
He'd gone and left her proper with a dose.*

She gave it to her father, who gave it to her mother
Who gave it to the Reverend Percy Brown.
He gave it to his cousin, who gave it to a dozen
And now it's halfway round the bloody town.

At last, it came to pass, it reached the sailor's arse,
It travelled half way up his bloody back
It rotted and it festered, his very life it pestered,
'Twas the vengeance of Talullah Johnstone Black.

There's a dirty stinking sailor to the north of Waterloo
With a dose of Syph that's slowly turning green
Though he's hacked it and he's scratched it
If he can e'er detach it, he's a better man than I am, GUNGA DIN.

THE HORSE AND THE COW

The horse and the cow live thirty years
And nothing know of wines or beers
The goats and sheep at twenty die
With never a taste of scotch or rye.
The sow drinks water by the ton
And at eighteen is nearly done
The dog at fifteen cashes in
Without the aid of rum or gin.
The cat in milk and water soaks
And then at twelve short years it croaks.
The modest sober home dry hen
Lays eggs for years and dies at ten.
All animals are strictly dry
They simply live and simply die.
But sinful, ginful rum-soaked men
Survive for three score years and ten.
And some of them, the mighty few
Stay pickled till they're ninety-two.

The carnal desires of the Camel
Are greater than anyone thinks
This perverted but passionate mammal
Has designs on the hole of the Sphinx
But at times this alluring depression
Is filled with the sands of the Nile
Which accounts for the camel's expression
And the Sphinx's inscrutable smile.

PICKLEDY PICKLEDY POX

Oh give me a home where the prostitutes roam
And your knackers hang down to your knees,
Where the babies are born with a fifteen inch
horn
And pox is the favourite disease.

Chorus: pickledy pickledy pox
pry the lid from the herring box,
you are never forlorn
when you're gilding the horn
at the brothel in East Grimsby Docks.

Oh give me a den that is mainly for men
Where the whore dance to fiddle and fife,
And they take down their drawers
For the Blacks and the Boers
It's the damndest hothouse of your life.

The beds they all creak and the ****pots all
leak
And the sheets are not always too clean,
But there's a hole in the floor
For the lame and the poor,
And for women a ******* machine.

THAT'S TORN IT

Little Mildred based her hopes
On a book by Marie Stopes
But to judge from her condition
She must have bought the wrong edition.

All the prophylactics planned
Cannot rid this wicked land
Of the overpopulation
Caused by careless copulation.

All the choicest wares of France
Cannot beat the laws of chance,
We would rather trust to luck
And so enjoy an honest ****.

TWENTY TOES

Here's to the game of twenty toes,
It's played all over the town,
The girls play it with ten toes up,
The boys with ten toes down.

I DREAMED MY LOVE LAY IN HER BED

I dreamed my love lay in her bed,
It was my chance to take her,
Her legs and arms abroad were spread,
She slept, I dared not wake her.
Oh pity it were that one so fair
Should crown her love with willow
The tresses of her golden hair
Did kiss her lonely pillow.
Methought her belly was a hill
Just like a mount of pleasure,
Under whose brow there grows a well,
Whose depth no man can measure.
About the pleasant mountain top,
There grew a lovely thicket,
Wherein my two hands travelled,
And raised a lively prickett.

They hunted there with happy noise,
About the ferny mountain,
Until heat the prickett forced to fly
And skip into the fountain.
The hounds they followed to the brink
And there at him they barked,
He plunged again but would not shrink.
His coming forth they waited.

Then forth he came as one half lame
Limp, weary, faint and tired,
And laid him down between her legs
For help he had required,
The hounds they were refreshed again,
My love from sleep returned,
And dreamed she held me in her arms,
And she was not alarmed.

A MINER COMING HOME ONE NIGHT

A miner coming home one night
Found his house without a light,
So he went upstairs to bed
And then a thought entered his head.

He went into his daughter's room
And found her hanging from a beam,
He took a knife and cut her down
And in her hand this note he found.

"My love is for a bold marine,
I always, always think of him,
And though he's far across the sea,
He never, never thinks of me.

So all you maidens bear in mind,
A good man's love is hard to find
Dig my grave both wide and deep
And rest my weary bones in sleep."

They dug her grave both wide and deep
And laid white lilies at her feet,
On her breast a turtle dove
To signify she died of love.

*Now there was an old lady who lived on our
street,
She got constipation through too much to eat.
She took several pills on a Saturday night
And soon she discovered she wanted to ******

*Chorus: Too-ra-la, Too-ra-lay,
          Oh a rolling stone gathers no moss, so
          they say,
          too-ra-lay, too-ra-lit,
          It's a ******* fine song but it's all
          about ****.*

*She went to her window and stuck out
her ****
But just then a night watchman happened to
pass;
He heard a loud noise as he looked up on high,
Then a bloody great **** hit him straight in
the eye.*

Chorus:

*He looked to the North, he looked to the
South,
And a bloody great lump landed right in his
mouth,
He looked to the East, he looked to the West,
And another great lump landed straight on his
chest.*

Chorus:

The next time you walk over Battersea Bridge,
Look out for a watchman asleep on the edge,
His chest bears a placard and on it is writ:
"Be kind to a watchman who is blinded by
****"

THERE WAS A PURITANICAL LAD

There was a puritanical lad
And he was called Matthias
Who wished to go to Rotterdam
To speak to Anannias.
He had not gone past half a mile
When he met a holy sister
And laid his Bible 'neath her ****
And happily he kissed her.

"Alas! what would the angels say?"
She said, "if they could see it!
My buttocks need some bolstering
So put the gospels under it!"
"But peace my love, before we part —
And I speak from sweet emotion,
For aye or any I'll have to stay
Until you taste my motions."

They ****** with glee with many a heave,
Until they both were tired,
"Alas," she cried, "you **** with glee,
And my petticoats are all mired.
If we are preachers of the Lamb
To the English congregation,
Either at Leyden or Amsterdam,
It must disgrace the nation.
But since it is, that part we must,
Though I am much unwilling,
Good brother, have another thrust,

And take from me this shilling,
To pay your way for many a day,
And feed your **** with filling.''
Then down she laid, that holy maid,
And drained him at a sitting.

THE TREE OF LIFE

Now prick up your ears and listen awhile,
For I'll tell you a tale that'll make you smile;
It's a faithful description of the tree of life,
So pleasing to ev'ry maid, widow and wife.

This tree is a succulent plant I declare,
Just having one straight stem, I swear,
Its top sometimes looks like a plum in May,
At other times more like a filbert, they say.

This tree universal all countries produce,
But till sixteen years' growth it's not fit for use,
Then nine or ten inches—perhaps even
higher,
And that's surely as much as a heart can
desire.

Its juice taken inward's a cure for the spleen,
And dispels in an instant the sickness called
Green,
Though sometimes it causes large tumours
below,
They disperse of themselves in nine months
or so.

It cures all dissensions between man and wife
And makes her feel pleasant in each stage of
life,
By right application it never will fail,
For then it is always put in through the tail.

Come, Ladies, that yearn for a sight of this tree,
Take this invitation and come here to me,
I have it right now at the peak of perfection
Ready for handling and fit for injection.

COME AWAY MY LOVE WITH ME

Come away my love with me,
To the station lavatory.
There is an expert there who can
Fill up three times the glittering pan.

The happy youth has no idea
He's suffering from diarrhoea,
Expelling clouds of noisome vapours
A fortune spent on toilet papers.

He tranquilly pursues his art
And shakes the building with a fart
O come away my love with me
To the station lavatory.

Strolling in a meadow green,
Flowers for to gather,
Where lilac ranks did stand on banks
To welcome comers thither,
I heard a voice which made a noise
And caused me to attend it,
I heard a lass say to a lad,
"Once more, and none can mend it."

They were so close together,
They made me much to wonder,
I know not which was whether,
Till I saw her under.
Then off he came and cried for shame,
Because so soon he'd ended,
Yet still she lies, and to him cries,
"Once more, and none can mend it!"

His looks were dull and very sad,
His courage she had tamed,
She bade him play the lusty lad
Or stop and be ashamed.
"So stiffly thrust and hit me just,
Fear not but freely spend it,
Play about, come in—come out,
Once more, and none can mend it!"

So then he thought to enter her,
Thinking the horn was on him,
But when he came to enter her,
The end turned back upon him.
She said, "O stay! Don't go away,
Although the end is bended,
But plunge again, and hit the vein,
Once more and none can mend it."

Then in her arms she did him fold,
And many times she kissed him,
But still his courage was too cold
For all the good she wished him.
With her soft hand she made it stand
So stiff she could not bend it,
And then again she cried, "Come on
Once more, and none can mend it!"

"Farewell, farewell, Sweetheart," he cried,
"For in faith I must be gone."
"Nay, then you do me wrong," she cried,
"To leave me so alone."
Away he went when all was spent,
And she was most offended;
Like a Trojan True she made a vow,
She'd soon have one to mend it!

CHICAGO

Chorus: I used to work in Chicago
*   In a department store,*
*   I used to work in Chicago,*
*   But I don't work there any more.*

A lady came into the hatshop,
I asked, "What kind would you like?"
"Felt," she said,
Felt I did,
I'll never work there any more.

A lady came in for a waterbottle,
I asked, "What kind would you like?"
"Rubber," she said,
Rub'er I did,
I'll never work there any more.

A lady came in for a sweater,
I asked, "What kind would you like?"
"Jumper," she said,
Jump'er I did,
I'll never work there any more.

A lady came in for a cake,
I asked, "What kind would you like?"
"Layer," she said,
Lay'er I did.
I'll never work there any more.

A lady came in for a ticket,
I asked, "Where would you like to go?"
"Bangor," she said,
Bang 'er I did,
I'll never work there any more.

A lady came in for a sleeper,
I asked, "Which berth would you like?"
"Upper," she said,
Up 'er I did,
I'll never work there any more.

TIM THE TINKER

The lady of the Manor
Was dressing for the ball
When she saw a Highland Tinker
******* up against the wall.

Chorus: With his bloody great kidney wiper
       And his ***** the size of three,
       And a yard-and-a-half of foreskin
       Hanging down below his knee.

The lady wrote a letter
And in it she did say,
She'd rather be ******* by a tinker
Than his Lordship any day.

Chorus

The Tinker got the letter
And when it he did read
His ***** began to fester
And his ***** began to bleed.

Chorus

He mounted on his donkey
And to her place did ride
With his ***** over shoulder
And his balls strapped to his side.

Chorus

*He ****** them in the parlour*
*He ****** them in the Hall*
The butler cried "Gawd Sive Us
*For he wants to **** us all."*

Chorus

*He ****** the Groom in the parlour*
And the Duchess in her pew
*But then he ****** the butler*
And the butler's pet mole too.

Chorus

Some say the Tinker's gone now,
*Gone ******* down to hell,*
*All set to **** the devil*
And we hope he does it well.

Chorus

I put my finger in the woodpecker's hole
And the woodpecker said, "God bless my soul,
Take it out,
Take it out,
Take it out,
Remove it."

I removed my finger from the woodpecker's
hole
And the woodpecker said, "God bless my
soul,
Put it back,
Put it back,
Put it back,
Replace it."

I replaced my finger in the woodpecker's hole
And the woodpecker said, "God bless my soul,
Turn it round,
Turn it round,
Turn it round,
Revolve it."

I revolved my finger in the woodpecker's hole
And the woodpecker said, "God bless my soul,
Pull it out,
Pull it out,
Pull it out,
Retract it."

*I retracted my finger from the woodpecker's
hole
And the woodpecker said, "God bless my soul,
Take a whiff,
Take a whiff,
Take a whiff,
Revolting."*

*My grandfather's **** was too long for his
jock,
So it dragged ninety yards on the floor;
It was bigger by far than the old man himself,
And it weighed not a pennyweight more.
With a horn on the morn of the day that he
was born,
And a horn on the day that he died,
My grandfather's **** was too long for his
jock,
So it stood for his honour and pride.*

LADY P*NKH*RST'S SPEECH

Extracts from Lady P*nkh*rst's speech in support of the Suffragettes in the House of Commons debate on Rights for Women:

"We want what men have. It may not be much but we want it. We will have it without friction, or, if we cannot have it through our organisations, we will have it through our combinations, or without them if necessary.

Men say we cannot grasp the potentialities, many and varied are men's arguments about us. They have driven their most prominent points into us again and again.

We refuse to be poked in the gallery and insist on being put down on the floor of the House.

Are we going to take it lying down? No.

Take it with our backs to the wall . . .

Some say 'Down with skirts,' but we say 'Up with skirts and down with trousers,' then we shall see things as they really are.

There is a little difference between man and woman.
(Voice in the Gallery 'Three cheers for the little difference.')

Furthermore, as long as we are split as we are, men will always get on top of us.

They block us in the House, they block us everywhere.

But we must change our position— we must get on top."

After this a man got up and pressed his point home. He won hands down.

LORD ST CLANCY

When Lord St Clancy became a nancy
It did not please the family fancy,
And so in order to protect him
They did inscribe upon his rectum,
"All commoners must now drive steerage,
*This ******** is reserved for peerage."*

The Mayor of Bayswater
Has got a pretty daughter

Chorus: And the hair on her diddy-di-dum
Hangs down to her knees,
One black one, one white one
And one with a little ***** on,
And the hair on her diddy-di-dum
Hangs down to her knees.

I've smelt it, I've felt it,
It felt like a bit of velvet.

I've seen it, I've seen it,
I've lain right between it.

She went to Glamorgan
Her **** like a barrelorgan.

If she were my daughter
I'd make her cut 'em shorter.

She slept with a demon
Who washed her with semen.

She lived on a mountain
And ****** like a bloody fountain

She stayed on a cattleranch
And **** like a bloody avalanche.

She bangs like a ****house door,
Swings back for more and more.

She sat on the window sill
And sucked till she had her fill

She married a Scotsman
Who tickled the ***** in 'em

She could take any *****
But the butcher's dog was thick.

She lived on malted milkshake
And rooted like a bloody rattlesnake.

He put his hand upon her toe, yoho, yoho,
He put his hand upon her toe, yoho, yoho
He put his hand upon her toe,
She said, "Marine, you're might slow
*Get in, get out, quit ******* about*
Yoho, yoho, yoho."

He put his hand upon her knee, yoho, yoho,
He put his hand upon her knee, yoho, yoho,
He put his hand upon her knee,
She said, "Marine, you're teasing me,
*Get in, get out, quit ******* about*
Yoho, yoho, yoho."

He put his hand upon her thigh, yoho, yoho,
He put his hand upon her thigh, yoho, yoho,
He put his hand upon her thigh,
She said, "Marine, you're mighty sly
*Get in, get out, quit ******* about*
Yoho, yoho, yoho."

He put his hand upon her snatch, yoho, yoho,
He put his hand upon her snatch, yoho, yoho,
He put his hand upon her snatch,
She said, "Marine, you're starting to scratch
*Get in, get out, quit ******* about*
Yoho, yoho, yoho."

He put his hand upon her tit, yoho, yoho,
He put his hand upon her tit, yoho, yoho,
He put his hand upon her tit,
She said, "Marine, squeeze it a bit,
Get in, get out, quit ******* about
Yoho, yoho, yoho."

And now she is in London town, yoho, yoho,
And now she is in London town, yoho, yoho,
She now she is in London town,
She's ******* the boys for miles around
Get in, get out, quit ******* about
Yoho, yoho, yoho.

And now she's in a wooden box, yoho, yoho,
And now she's in a wooden box, yoho, yoho,
And now she's in a wooden box,
She died from too much Marine Corps ***.
Get in, get out, quit ******* about
Yoho, yoho, yoho.

PLEASE DO NOT TREAD ON MY BALLS

Please do not tread on my balls
Please do not tread on my balls
I am aware that they hang too low
Should have been cut off ten years ago
I have what some people call
Simply phenomenal balls
So please do not tread on my balls, balls, balls,
balls.

LETITIA HAS A LARGE ONE

Letitia has a large one, and so has cousin Luce,
Eliza has a small one though large enough for
use.

Beneath a soft and glossy curl, each Lass has
one in front,
To find it in an animal, you at the tail must
hunt.

A child may have a little one enclosed within
a clout,
In fact all females have one, no girl is born
without.

All fowls have one (not cocks of course) and
though prolific breeders
The fact that fish have none at all is known to
piscine breeders.

Hermaphrodites have none, Mermaids are
minus too,
Nell Gwynn possessed a double share if books
we read are true.

It's used by all in Nuptial Bliss, in Carnal
Pleasures found.
Destroy it, Life becomes extinct; the world is
but a sound.

Lasciviousness here has its source, Harlots its use apply.
Without it Lust has never been, and even Love would die.

Now tell me what this wonder is, but Pause before you guess it
If you are Mother, maid or man, I swear you don't possess it.

Answer: The letter "L".

THE CHANDLER'S BOY

The Boy went into the Chandler's shop
Some matches for to buy
He looked around, around he looked
But no one did he spy.
He cried aloud, aloud he cried
With a voice to wake the dead
When he heard a kind of a "Rat-tat-tat"
Right above his head.
When he heard a kind of "Rat-tat-tat"
Right above his head.

Now the boy was of an enquiring mind
So he quietly climbed the stair
And the door of the room was open
And the Chandler's wife was there
The Chandler's wife lay on the bed
A man between her thighs
And they were having a "Rat-tat-tat"
Right before his eyes
And they were having a "Rat-tat-tat"
Right before his eyes.

Oh boy, oh boy, my secret keep
And for me tell a lie
For if the chandler should hear of this
He'd beat me till I cry.
And if you promise to be good

I'll always to you be kind
And you shall have a "Rat-tat-tat"
Whenever you feel inclined
And you shall have a "Rat-tat-tat"
Whenever you feel inclined.

The Chandler returned and entered the shop
He quickly smelt a rat
Seeing his wife all naked there
Her hand upon her ****
The Chandler's wife ran from the room
Expecting the boy had fled
But he was having a "Rat-tat-tat"
All by himself in bed,
But he was having a "Rat-tat-tat"
All by himself in bed.

Now I'm fond of *******; it is my delight.
I once ****** a girl forty times in one night.
And each time I ****** her I came quite a
quart
If you don't call that *******, you
******* well ought.

The Orderly sergeant says "Look here my lad,
You're late on parade and your turn out is bad
I've seen things like you behind bars in the
zoo."
I replied "**** them all and to start with,
**** you."

The Officer looked at the horses today
He inspected my charger and then he did say
"This horse is too thin and it's got a bad
cough."
I replied "You're too fat and you'd better
**** off."

There was a young man named Archibald
Clare
And he was very populaire
For he was a famous jugulaire
And used to play with his balls.

Chorus: For they were large balls, balls as
heavy as lead
he gave them a flick with the end of
his *****
And swung them right over his head.

As he was walking down the street
Little Miss Brown he chanced to meet
Walking along with a dog at her feet
As he twisted and twirled his balls.

As he was swinging them round and round
Down they came with a hell of a bound
Right on top of the faithful hound
Who was watching him play with his balls.

Now Little Miss Brown was overwrought
And swore she'd take the case to court
For in her opinion no man ought
To be twisting and twirling his balls.

They took him to a magistrate
Who put him in a cell in State
And left him there to meditate
On how to play with his balls.

And when they took the case to court
The lawyer of the lady sought
To prove that Archibald didn't ought
To twist and twirl his balls

The jury said 'twas a bloody disgrace
Exposing yourself in a public place
Wagging your tool in a lady's face
And twisting and twirling your balls.

The judge and jury couldn't agree
And the judge he said "It's plain to see
And really and truly I cannot see
Why a man shouldn't play with his balls."

Then Archibald gave the court a shock
Bold as brass he left the dock
Swinging his balls around his ****
Twirling and twisting his *****

And this is the moral of this song
If you play with your balls you can't go wrong
So bang your ***** against a gong
And twiddle and play with your balls.

My wife, my maid and I; my wife, my maid and I
Went out one night to do a *****
But the maid **** more than I.

My wife was grieved at this, my wife was grieved at this
Said she to me "If you'll agree
We'll challenge the bitch to ****."

Three **** pots came to call, three **** pots came to call
But she opened her sluices and let out her juices
And bloody near flooded the hall.

This broke my poor wife's heart, this broke my poor wife's heart
Said she to me "If you'll agree
We'll challenge the bitch to fart."

Such farting ne'er was heard, such farting ne'er was seen
For that girl with a *** like a musical drum
She farted "God Save The Queen".

MRS PUGGY WUGGY

Mrs Puggy Wuggy has a square cut punt
Not a punt cut square
Just a square cut punt
It's round in the stern and blunt in the front
Mrs Puggy Wuggy has a square cut punt.

THE HEDGEHOG

The exhaustive and careful enquiries
Of Darwin and Huxley and Ball
Have conclusively proved that the Hedgehog
Can hardly be buggered at all
But further most painful researches
Have incontrovertibly shown
That this state of comparative safety
Is enjoyed by the Hedgehog alone.

THE BREAKFAST SONG

The gong was sounded for breakfast
By the butler so portly and stout
And Ma came down with a pot full of ****
And Pa with his ***** hanging out.

You're behaving quite nicely, said Mother
Though seldom it's my way to boast
Well, manners be buggered, said Father
And tossed himself off in the toast.

And Peter he ****** in the pepper
And Spencer he spent in a spoon
While Mother let out such a hell of a ****
That Father could scarce keep the tune.

Then John shoved a sausage up Susie
And laughed loud and long at the joke
And Ma asked Pa to **** in his hat
So that baby could play with the smoke.

We are three harlots of Baghdad
We **** and fornicate like mad
We don't give a rap
For a dose of the clap
Our object is to spread disease
Syphilee, gonorhee
Our object is to spread disease.

You can have it standing up or lying down
You can have it either way for half-a-crown
Up the back, up the front
Up the navel, up the ****
We personally recommend a bit of brown
Syphilee, gonorhee
Our object is to spread disease.

LITTLE REDWING

There was once an Indian Maid
And she was sore afraid
That the big buckeroo
Would ram it up her flue
As on the bed she laid.

So she filled her snatch with sand
And held it in her hand
Lest the big buckeroo
Should ram it up her flue
And reach the promised land.

Oh, the moon shines bright on Little Redwing
As she lay sleeping
There came a-creeping
'Twas the buckeroo with eyes a-peeping
Under the flap of Redwing's tepee.

Now that buckeroo was wise
He slipped between her thighs
With an old gum boot
Pulled over his root
He made Little Redwing open her eyes.

She reached for her bowie knife
To fight for her dear life
With one fell flick
Went his ******** and his ****
And his pegging days were over.

Now the sun shines bright on Little Redwing
As she lays yawning
There hangs a warning
Two balls and a ***** adorning
The flap of Redwing's tepee.

I had twelve bottles of whisky in my cellar, and my wife ordered me to empty the contents of each and every bottle down the sink, so I proceeded to do as my wife desired and withdrew the cork from the first bottle, poured the contents down the sink, with the exception of one glass, which I drank.

I then withdrew the cork from the second bottle and did likewise, with the exception of one glass, which I drank.

I extracted the cork from the third bottle, emptied the good old booze down the bottle, except a glass, which I devoured.

I pulled the cork from the third sink, and poured the bottle down the glass, when I drank some.

I pulled the bottle from the cork of the next one, drank one sink out of it, and then threw the rest down the sink.

I pulled the sink out of the next cork, and poured the bottle down my neck.

I pulled the next bottle down my throat, and poured the cork down the sink, all but the sink which I drank.

I pulled the next cork from my throat, and poured the sink down the bottle and drank the cork.

Well, I had them all emptied and steadied the house with one hand, and counted the bottles which were twenty-four, so counted them again and I had seventy-four, and as the houses came round I counted them and finally I had all the houses and bottles counted, and I proceeded to wash the bottle, and I couldn't get the brush in the bottles, so I turned them inside out and washed and wiped them all, and went upstairs and told my other half all about which I did, and Oh Boy!

I've got the wifest little nice in the world.

THE PIG GOT UP AND WALKED AWAY

*One evening in October, when I was far from
sober
To keep my feet from wandering I tried
My poor legs were all a-flutter, so I lay down
in the gutter;
And a pig came up and lay down by my side.
We sang "Never mind the weather just as
long as we're together"
Till a lady passing by was heard to say
"You can tell a man who boozes by the
company he chooses"
And the pig got up and slowly walked away.*

*Yes the pig got up and slowly walked away
Slowly walked away, slowly walked away
Yes the pig got up and then smiled and winked
at me
As he slowly walked away.*

*On cattle shows I've centred, in one a pig I
entered
And one day I sat down with him in his sty
Famous people came to visit, when a sweet
voice said "What is it?"
I looked up and Greta Garbo caught my eye.*

She said "What a lofely fella," poked the pig
with her umbrella
The she looked at me awhile and whispered,
"Say!
Yeah, ay tank dis iss hees brudder"——at my
side I felt a shudder
And the pig got up and slowly walked away.

Yes the pig got up and slowly walked away
Slowly walked away, slowly walked away.
Yes the pig got up, and then smiled and
winked at me
As he slowly walked away.

THE VALLEYS OF ASSAM

I've crapped in the valleys of Assam
I've pissed in the plains of Cawnpore,
Cawnpore
And I've often passed wind in the desert of
Sind
And I've slept with a Calcutta whore.

I've belched near the Tropic of Cancer
Stink-finger I've played in Madrid, Madrid
Put a girl in Bombay in the family way
And refused to acknowledge the kid.

I've seduced little virgins in China,
I've taught self-abuse in Japan, Japan,
And when hard up for oats upon City Line
boats
I've had to resort to a man.

I've bathed in the nude at Llandudno
I've fondled my foreskin out West, out West,
And I've played soixante-neuf on Parisian turf
And I've belly-rubbed tarts in Trieste.

I've tickled the tits of a Nautch Girl
I've French-kissed young women from Wales,
from Wales
And I've played with my balls at Niagara
Falls,
And I've been gamerouched in Marseilles.

I've split several ***** in Karachi
I've smacked bitches' bums on the pier, the
pier
But what now fans the fire of my ardent desire
Is to bugger a goat in Kashmire.

JUNGLE MENU

*A Cannibal Mother cooking lunch, for her
little Cannibal boy,
Said, "Here's a treat, I've got some meat,
I know you will enjoy.*

*Boiled ***** and ********, boiled
***** and ********,
That's the stuff for your Darbykell,
Makes you fight and **** like hell!
Those English Lords eat fish and chips,
When dining in their castles,
But we like ***** and ******** Stew,
And Rissoles from ********."*

BEDTIME STORY

Sandman is coming, all the world is still,
Take the little darling up the wooden hill,
Kiss the little angel, blow the candle out,
Tip toe across the room, (shhh),
And the bastard starts to shout:

Chorus: Tell me a story, tell me a story,
Tell me 'bout the brothel that me
Auntie used to keep.
Tuck me in my little bed, stroke my
little tousled head,
Tell me a story and I'll go to
******* sleep!

Tell me a story, tell me a story,
Tell me 'bout when auntie used to fiddle with
your flies,
Where's me poofy uncle Frank, show me how
to have a wank,
Tell me a story, and I'll close me *******
eyes.

Tell me a story, tell me a story,
Tell me 'bout when dearest, darling Mummy
was a cow,
Tell me 'bout me Auntie Marge, tell me what
she used to charge,
Tell me a story, and I'll stop me *******
row!

CHRISTOPHER AND ALICE

Inside the yard at Buckingham Palace,
Christopher Robin went down to Alice,
"Dear little Chistopher knows his stuff,
At 'Trying the Beard' and 'Noshing the
muff'," says Alice.

Inside the yard at Buckingham Palace,
Christopher Robin's still gobblin' Alice,
"One more time, then after lunch,
I'll reciprocate, and 'Munch the Trunch',"
says Alice.

Christopher Robin has got his knob in,
Alice is down and she's gobblin' Robin.
She won't say a word, while 'Tongue-ing the
****',
"'Cos it's rude to talk, when your mouth is
full," says Alice.

They're plating hard at Buckingham Palace,
Alice plates Robin and Robin plates Alice,
They're lying down upon the turf,
"Nothing compares with a Soixante Neuf,"
says Alice.

PISSING OVER THE RIVER

I'm a fun loving boy, and I always enjoy,
Just pissing about on the river,

Watching the stunts of the ***** in the punts
Who're pissing about on the river.

Cheering the eights as they finish the course,
They loosen their rollocks, and lay on their
oars,

The victorious eight is awarded a plate,
For pissing about on the river.

The girls wait to welcome the crews at the
locks,
They all love a stroke, now they're kissing the
Cox.

I row to the bank, and I have a quick wank,
While pissing about on the river.

WALKING DOWN CRUMLIN

As I was walking down Crumlin one day,
Singing "How are you, darlin', how are you?"
I met a young lady all dressed grey,
Singing, "How do you do, darlin', do?"

She gave me a toss of her curly locks
Singing "How are you, darlin', how are you?"
I gave her a shilling, she gave me the pox,
Singing "How do you do, darlin', do?"

So off to the doctor next morning I go,
Singing, "How are you, darlin', how are you?"
My **** and my ******** I had to
show,
Singing "How do you do, darlin', do?"

A nurse came in with a poultice red-hot,
Singing "How are you, darlin', how are you?"
"Put this on your ******** before they drop
off!"
Singing "How do you do, darlin', do?"

The doctor came in with a ******* great
lance,
Singing "How are you, darlin', how are you?"
"You poxy-faced bastard, I'll make you
dance!"
Singing "How do you do, darlin', do?"

Now, I am well and free from pain,
Singing "How are you, darlin', how are you?"
If I had a shilling, I'd **** *her again,*
Singing, "How do you do, darlin', do?"

THE DILL-DOLDRUMS

You sold me my Dill-Doll a year ago,
Yes, you did, for a quid, yes, you did.
You told me it was safe, but now I know.
'Twas under the pillow in my hotel,
The chambermaid found it and enjoyed it, as
well.
She told her friends, and they all took their
turn.
My secret weapon went from hole to hole,
And now my favourite chap, has gone down
with the (CLAP HANDS),
That I got from my old Dill-Doll.

MOTHER KELLY'S WHORESHOP

In Mother Kelly's Whoreshop, down Paradise
Row,
I'd **** along o' Nellie, she'd gobble long o'
Joe.
She'd get a little hold of me ****
And poke it through the hole in her frock
Where her **** showed through,
Her belly was the fattest down our Alley.

To Mother Kelly's Whoreshop I often go,
I'm always welcome, and the price is low, I
know,
Because they love it just like I do,
In Mother Kelly's Whoreshop, down Paradise
Row.

TOGETHER

*We strolled the lanes together, shagged all the
Janes together
Blocked up their drains together,
He was just my friend, but it had to end,
One day we tried together, to get inside
together
He got tangled with me, and from now on, we
three
We always will be, together.*

A strange bird, the cuckoo, he sits on the grass,
*His wings neatly folded, his beak up his ****,*
In this strange position, he murmurs, "Twit,
twit",
'Cos it's hard to sing, "Cuckoo!"
*With a beak full of ****.*

*John Brown's ***** was a bloody awful sight,*
Mucked about with gonorrhoea and buggered
*up with ****
The agonies of syphilis kept him awake all
night,
But he still went rogering along.

Chorus: Oh, the hoary old seducer,
Oh, the hoary old seducer,
Oh, the hoary old seducer,
He still went rogering along!

The colour of his water was a sort of
orange-ade,
Little gonorrhoea germs within his scrotum
played,
In spite of these inconveniences, he went on
undismayed,
Yes he still went rogering along.

Chorus

Girls would come from miles around, to his
Baronial Hall,
*To see his giant ***** and his one remaining*
*****,*
*And see the rows of ******heads all hung*
around the wall,
But he still went rogering along.

Chorus

DAN, THE WATERWORKS MAN

I'm Dan, Dan, the waterworks man, the man
wot stops your water.
I work all day, and half the night,
Calling out, "Missus, is your water all right?"
I ain't the bloke wot brings your coke,
I ain't a railway porter,
I'm Dan, Dan, the Waterworks man,
The man wot stops your water.

THREE JEWS OF NORFOLK

There were three Jews of Norfolk
There were three Jews of Norfolk
NOR-OR-OR-OR-FOLK-FOLK-FOLK
NOR-OR-OR-OR-FOLK-FOLK-FOLK
There were three Jews of Norfolk.

The first one's name was Isaac
The first one's name was Isaac
EYE-EYE-SUCK-SUCK-SUCK
EYE-EYE-SUCK-SUCK-SUCK
The first one's name was Isaac.

The second one's name was Joseph
The second one's name was Joseph
JOSIE-JOSIE-SIPH-SIPH-SIPH
JOSIE-JOSIE-SIPH-SIPH-SIPH
The second one's name was Joseph.

The third one's name was Jehosaphat
The third one's name was Jehosaphat
JEHOSO-JEHOSO-FART-FART-FART
JEHOSO-JEHOSO-FART-FART-FART
The third one's name was Jehosophat.

They went for a ride in a charabanc
They went for a ride in a charabanc
CHARA-CHARA-BANG-BANG-BANG
CHARA-CHARA-BANG-BANG-BANG
They went for a ride in a charabanc.

There was a mighty thunder clap
There was a mighty thunder clap
THUNDER-THUNDER-CLAP-CLAP-
CLAP
THUNDER-THUNDER-CLAP-CLAP-
CLAP
There came a mighty thunder clap.

They swerved into a precipice
They swerved into a precipice
PRECI-PRECI-PISS-PISS-PISS
PRECI-PRECI-PISS-PISS-PISS
They swerved into a precipice.

They were taken to a hospital
They were taken to a hospital
HOSPI-HOSPI-TOOL-TOOL-TOOL
HOSPI-HOSPI-TOOL-TOOL-TOOL
They were taken to a hospital.

But there were no beds vacant
But there were no beds vacant
VAY-AY-AY-AY-****-****-****
VAY-AY-AY-****-**** ****
But there were no beds vacant.

This is where we finish it
This is where we finish it
FINI-FINI-****-****-****
FINI-FINI-****-****-****
This is where we finish it.

*Chorus: Oh, we're off to see the Wild West
Show
The elephant and the kangaroo
Never mind the weather
As long as we're together
We're off to see the Wild West Show.*

*Now here, ladies and gentlemen, in the first
cage we have the laughing hyena. This
animal lives in the mountains and once every
year comes down to eat. Once every two years
he comes down to drink and once every three
years he comes down for sexual intercourse.
What the ****** hell he has to laugh about,
I don't know.*

Chorus

*And in the next cage we have the giraffe. This
creature is the most popular animal in the
animal kingdom. Why? Every time he goes
into a bar he says "The highballs are on me."*

Chorus

*And here, ladies and gentlemen, we have the
Urangutang. As this animal proceeds from
branch, swinging through the forest, his balls
urang-u-tang, urang-u-tang.*

Chorus

And in the next cage we have the Oster-reich. This animal, at the first sign of danger, buries its head in the sand and whistles through the whole of the afternoon.

Chorus

And in the next cage we have the Rhino Sauras. This animal is reputed to be the richest in the world. Its name is derived from the Latin—rhino meaning money and sore**** meaning piles, hence piles of money.

Chorus

And here we have the Keerie Bird. This bird lives in the Antarctic. And every time it comes in to land on the ice, says "Keerie, keerie, keer-ist its cold."

Chorus

And in the next cage we have the leopard. Yes, the leopard on its coat has one spot for every day of the year. What about a Leap Year? George, lift up the leopard's tail.

Chorus

And in this cage we have the Winky Wanky Bird. By some strange happening, the nervous system of this bird's eyelids is connected to its foreskin. Every time it winks, it wanks and every time it wanks, it winks. You, boy, stop throwing sand in the bird's eyes.

Chorus

And here is the elephant. The elephant has a ginormous appetite. In one day it eats two tons of hay, one dozen bunches of bananas and twenty buckets of rice. Madam, don't stand too near the elephant's backside. Madam— madam. Too late. George, dig her out.

Chorus

And here, ladies and gentlemen, we have the Oozle Woozle Bird. These birds fly in a line ahead formation and, at the first sign of danger, the last bird flies up the **** of the bird in front and so on up the line. The remaining bird then flies round in ever decreasing circles, finally disappearing up its own orifice from which position it proceeds to shower **** and derision in all directions.

Chorus

And in the next cage we have the Triangular. This animal has a triangular orifice—hence the Pyramids and the sign of the Y.W.C.A.

Chorus: Oh, we're off to see the Wild West Show
  The elephant and the kangaroo
  Never mind the weather
  As long as we're together
  We're off to see the Wild West Show.

THE VICAR IN THE DOCKYARD CHURCH

*The vicar in the dockyard church, one Sunday
morning said
Some dirty bastard's **** himself. I'll punch
his ******* head.
Then up jumped Jock, from the third row
back, and he spat a might go-o-o-ob
I'm the one who's **** himself, you can chew
my ******* kno-o-o-ob
You can chew my ******* knob.*

*The organist played Hearts of Oak, mixed up
with Auld Lang Syne
The preacher then got up and said, you have
had your ******* time
The organist walked down the aisle with his
organ on his ba-a-a-ack
Then up jumped Jock and hollered out, you
can waltz that bastard ba-a-a-ack
You can waltz that bastard back.*

Chorus: We'll have a drink, a drink, a drink,
With Lydia Pink, a Pink, a Pink,
Saviour of the human race
For she's invented a vegetable compound
And all the papers they publish her face.

Now Mr Brown had a very small penis
He could hardly raise a stand
So they gave him the vegetable compound
Now he comes in either hand.

Chorus

Now Master Brown had very small knackers
They were just like a couple of peas
So they gave him the vegetable compound
Now they hang below his knees.

Chorus

Now Mrs Brown had invisible bosoms
They scarcely showed beneath her blouse
So they gave her the vegetable compound
Now they milk her with the cows.

Chorus

COLD

As cold as a frog in an ice-bound pool
As cold as the knob of an Eskimo's tool
As cold as an icicle all glossy and glum
As cold as the fringe round a polar bear's bum
As cold as charity, and that's bloody chilly,
But not so cold as our poor Milly—She's dead.

CHIN-CHIN CHINAMAN

Chin-Chin, Chinaman, walking down the Strand
Stony-broke, wants a poke, penis in his hand
Up comes Poxy Lil: he doesn't care a rap
Three days later Clap, clap clap.

The first time I saw her, she was all dressed in
red
All in red, all in red.
I snatched her maiden-head
Down in the valley where she followed me.

Chorus: Fol di rol, fol di rol,
Fol di rol, fol di rol,
A rolling stone gathers no moss, so
they say,
But a standing stone gets pissed on.

The next time I saw her, she was all dressed in
white
All in white, all in white,
I had her twice that night
Down in the valley where she followed me.

Chorus

The third time I saw her she was dressed all in
green,
All in green, all in green.
I filled her soup tureen,
Down in the valley where she followed me.

Chorus

The fourth time I saw her, she was dressed all
in puce,
All in puce, all in puce,

She rolled back my prepuce,
Down in the valley where she followed me.

Chorus

The fifth time I saw her, she was all dressed in
blue,
All in blue, all in blue,
I had a good blow through
Down in the valley where she followed me.

Chorus

The sixth time I saw her, she was all dressed in
black,
All in black, all in black.
I took her up the back,
Down in the valley where she followed me.

Chorus

The last time I saw her, she was dressed all in
check,
All in check, all in check,
*I wrung her ******* neck,*
Down in the valley where she followed me.

Chorus

Mary in the kitchen punching duff, punching duff, punching duff
Mary in the kitchen punching duff,

BULLSHITE

Mary in the kitchen punching duff,
When the cheeks of her **** went chuff,
chuff, chuff
**** all round the room tra-la
**** all round the room

Mary in the kitchen boiling rice, boiling rice,
boiling rice,
Mary in the kitchen boiling rice.

BULLSHITE

Mary in the kitchen boiling rice
When out of her **** jumped three blind
mice,
**** all round the room tra-la
**** all round the room

Mary in the kitchen shelling peas, shelling
peas, shelling peas
Mary in the kitchen shelling peas.

BULLSHITE

Mary in the kitchen shelling peas,
The hairs of her **** hung down to her
knees,

**** *all round the room tra-la*
**** *all round the room.*

Mary in the garden sifting cinders, sifting
cinders, sifting cinders
Mary in the garden sifting cinders.

BULLSHITE

Mary in the garden sifting cinders
Blew one fart and broke ten windows
**** *all round the room tra-la*
**** *all round the room*

Mary had a dog whose name was Ben, name
was Ben, name was Ben
Mary had a dog whose name was Ben,

BULLSHITE

Mary had a dog whose name was Ben.
*Had one **** which worked like ten*
**** *all round the room tra-la*
**** *all round the room.*

Mary in the kitchen baking cakes, baking
cakes, baking cakes,
Mary in the kitchen baking cakes,

BULLSHITE

Mary in the kitchen baking cakes
When out of her tits came two milk shakes
**** *all round the room tra-la*
**** *all round the room.*

*Gather round once again you buggers and
bawds
Give ear to my story and mark well my words,
For the testament old and the gospels so new
Contain no recital more faithful and true.*

*There were four merry maidens in Warwick
did dwell,
Four practical jokers, as the story will tell,
And such was their humour, and such were
their wits
That it fell to their mind to plague Jack with
the *******.*

*Now Jack was the groom and it was his delight
To dine off sweet pudding and treacle each
night,
So Lilly the cook to the kitchen did steal
And mixed syrup of figs with his evening
meal.*

*Jack he came in his new buckskin pants
And he gulped down his meal with scarcely a
glance,
So very soon after his trouble did start
Announced to the public at large with a fart.*

*After that the deluge, for a moment deferred
And a rushing and flushing of impatient turd*

The buckskins were new and the buttons were tight,
And before he could drop them they were bulging with ****.

Poor Jack staggered out scarcely able to think,
Clutching his guts and half faint with the stink.
And for three days and nights he was locked in the lav.
A-brooding over what vengeance he'd have.

A week or two later while out in the barn
He saw an old gypsy approaching the farm,
"What do you come for, old woman?" he cried
"I'm come to read young ladies' palms," she replied.

"Young ladies," cursed Jack, "By Hell's bitter cup
They're the very same ***** *who buggered me up."*
Now here was the chance to give vengeance a start
So he bribed the old hag for her clothes and her cart.

Well, in for a penny and in for a pound,
The biter is bit and the grinder is ground,

When this dirty old hag took her fast by the hand
Young Lilly the cook never knew what was planned.

"I see from your hand that you're tender and mild,"
Said Jack, and he added: "You'll soon be with child.
And just to be sure how the future, will be,
Let us look at the Blue Vein' twixt navel and knee."

Lilly laughed in derision, for though somewhat a flirt
Her maidenhead till that day had suffered no hurt,
But she soon changed her tune, for Jack ever so quick
Had ripped down her knickers and stuffed in his *****.

Susan was next and she proffered her paw
Little suspecting what fate had in store.
"Your's future's uncertain, there may be some pain
But for certain opinion let's see your Blue Vein."

Before she could answer he'd lifted her robe
And without much ado her future did probe,

And when it was done said: "Your future is
clear,
But I can't see your Blue Vein, 'tis covered
in hair."

Annie was next, a prim little prude,
"Your future," said Jack, "begins in the
nude,"
And before she could utter a cry of disgust
He had upped her and tupped her and pulled
out his lust.

The last of the ladies was chambermaid Pris,
"Your future," said Jack, "begins with a kiss
It begins with a kiss and it ends with a ****"
And quick as a twinkle her Blue Vein did
block.

That was the tale of the Blue Vein, my friend,
And the moral, as always, I've left to the end.
Spare young Jack, pretty maidens, your
chicaneries for
If you meddle behind he may meddle before.

I LAID MY HAND UPON HER KNEE

I laid my hand upon her knee
She said: "Young man you're very free."

Chorus: With your hand, with your hand,
*   With your H-A-N-D hand.*

I laid my hand upon her toe,
She said: "Young man you're very low."

I put my hand upon her calf,
She said: "Young man you're there by half."

I put my hand upon her thigh,
She said: "Young man you're getting rather
high."

I put my hand upon her rear,
She said: "Young man you're getting rather
near."

I put my hand upon her ***,
She said: "Young man you'd better use your
thumb."

So I laid my hand upon her ****,
And she said: "Young man you'd better put
it in."

So I popped it in and waggled it about,
And she said, "Young man, you'd better take
it out."

THE LOBSTER

Fisherman, fisherman,
Home from the sea,
Have you a lobster
You will sell to me

Chorus: Roll tiddly oh
**** or bust,
Never let your *******
Dangle in the dust.

Yes sir, yes sir, I have two,
And the biggest of the bastards
I will sell to you.

So I took the lobster home
But I couldn't find a dish,
So I put it in a place,
Where the missus has a ****.

Early in the morning
As you all know
The missus got up
To let the water flow.

First there was a yell,
Then there came a grunt,
And out came the missus,
With the lobster in her ****.

The missus grabbed the brush
And I grabbed the broom,
And we chased the ******* lobster
Round and round the room.

Oh we hit it on the head
And we hit it on the side,
We hit the ******* lobster
Till it nearly died.

Oh the story has a moral.
And the moral is this,
Always have a shuftie
Before you have a ****.

This is the ending of the song
And should you ask for more,
There's an apple up my ****,
And you can have the core.

*She wears her silk pyjamas in the summer
when it's hot,
She wears a woollen nightie in the winter when
it's not,
But later in the springtime and early in the fall
But jumps into bed with nothing on at all.*

*Chorus: She's a most immoral lady,
She's a most immoral lady,
She's a most immoral lady,
As she lay between the sheets
With nothing on at all.*

*Oh Sir Jasper do not touch me,
Oh Sir Jasper do not touch me,
Oh Sir Jasper do not touch me,
As she lay between the sheets
With nothing on at all.*

*Glory, glory Hallelujah,
See the devil coming to yer,
He's going to put his pitchfork through yer,
For jumping into bed with nothing on at all.*

TIDDLY-WINKS OLD MAN

Tiddly-winks old man
Put your ******** in a can,
If you can't find a woman,
Find a good clean man.

THE DUCHESS OF LEE

Said the Duchess of Lee once at tea,
"Young man, do you fart when you pee?"
I replied with some wit,
"Do you belch when you ****?"
I think that was one up to me.

I dined with the Duchess of Lee,
She said: "Will you lie down with me?"
I replied with some tact
"As a matter of fact
I have brought a French letter with me."

So I lay with the Duchess of Lee,
Her manner was open and free,
Her words to me were:
"Which do you prefer,
My **** or my ****?"

I examined the Duchess of Lee,
To see just which side it would be,
I examined her front,
She'd a nice little ****,
But I found it too narrow for me.

I turned over the Duchess of Lee,
And examined her backside with glee,
And oh my delight
When I found it just right
So I lay with the Duchess of Lee.

I awoke with the Duchess of Lee,
And she said, "I'm sure you'll agree,
That orifice fundamental
Though less than sentimental
Is safer and better for me."

MARY BOX

This is the tale of Mary Box
Who gave a thousand men the pox,
Soldiers and sailors and men of honour
Fought like fiends to climb upon her,
And now she's dead she's not forgotten,
They dig her up and stuff her rotten.

MY LITTLE PINK PANTIES

I wore my panties, my little pink panties
And he wore his G.I. shorts.
He began to caress me
And then he undressed me,
What a thrill we had in store.
He played with my titties
My little pink titties
And down where the short hairs grow.
His kisses grew sweeter
He pulled out his Peter
And whitewashed my little red rose.

MY OLD FLO

My old Flo has a fancy for buggery,
Up her **** she can take a pretty load,
Now she's opened an academy for sodomy
Down at the bottom of the old Kings Road.

First lady forward, second lady back,
Third lady's finger up the fourth lady's crack.
Don't get them mixed up, the short with the
tall,
Lady with the bad breath, face to the wall.

NEVER WED AN OLD MAN

An old man came courtin' me,
Hey ding doorum dow,
An old man came courtin' me,
Hey doorum dow,
An old man came courtin' me,
Fain would he marry me,
Maids when you're young
Never wed an old man.

Chorus: For he's got no faloral faldiddle
        faloorum,
        For he's got no faloorum faldiddle
        faldey,
        He's got no faloorum
        He's lost his ding doorum
        So maids when you're young
        Never wed an old man.

When we went to the church
Hey ding doorum dow,
When we went to the church,
Hey doorum dow,
When we went to the church,
He left me in the lurch,
Maids when you're young never wed
Never wed an old man.

When we went up to bed
Hey ding doorum dow,
When we went up to bed,
Hey doorum dow,
When we went up to bed,
He neither done nor said,
Maid when you're young,
Never wed an old man.

Now when he went off to sleep,
Hey ding doorum dow,
When he went off to sleep,
Hey doorum dow,
When he went off to sleep
Out of bed I did creep,
Into the arms of a jolly young man.

And I found his falooral faldiddle faloorum,
I found his faloorum faldiddle faldey,
He's got my ding doorum
So maids when you're young
Never wed an old man.

OLD BOY

With baited breath the dean undressed
The vicar's wife to lie on.
He thought it crude to do it nude
So he kept the old school tie on.

Oh, once I had a girl, had a girl,
Oh, once I had a girl, had a girl,
Oh, once I had a girl, she put me in a whirl.
Put your shoulder next to mine and pump
away, pump away
Put your shoulder next to mine and pump
away.

She had me on a string
And I bought her everything.

When I came home from sea
I bought her gifts so free.

I bought her presents one,
She said I shouldn't have done.

I bought her presents two,
And her heart she let me woo.

I bought her presents three,
And she caught me by the lee.

I bought her presents four,
And she met me on the shore.

I bought her presents five,
And she was very much alive.

I bought her presents six,
And that one did the trick.

I bought her presents seven
And she said she was in heaven.

I bought her presents eight,
And I took her for my mate.

I bought her presents nine,
And the baby's doing fine.

I bought her presents ten,
And she said "Let's start again."

THE WOMEN OF PAPUA

If you are a woman in Papua,
You'd better not leave
Your door ajar.
If you do you'll find you are
Bearing the burden in Papua.

Native women in Papua
Something about them co-la-la
Maybe its because they wear no bra
Bearing the burden in Papua.

Tropical diseases in Papua
Oh my God, they're the worst by far,
Diarrhoea, dysentery, malaria,
Bearing the burden in Papua.

LAST NIGHT I PULLED ME PUD

Last night I pulled me pud,
It did me good, I knew it would.
Sling it,
Fling it,
Throw it on the floor,
Smash it,
Crash it,
Catch it in the door,
Some people say,
That *******'s mighty good,
But for personal enjoyment,
I'd rather pull me pud.

LITTLE JIM

Now here's a pretty little tale so hear it if you
will,
It's about a little fellow one night on Tooting
Hill,
He was spawned on Tooting Hill my boys,
but born in Camberwell,
And when he popped out he gave a shout:
"The Old Man ****** her well!"

Chorus: Little Jim, content with masturbation
   Little Jim, playing with his ****,
   Little Jim, content with simple
   frigging,
   Thought a **** was something you
   were called at grammar school.

Now down at Selsey Manor there was a great
ado,
For he buggered all the prefects and all the
masters too,
But at last he was expelled or so the records
say,
For tossing off the D*ke of K*nt on
Coronation Day.

Chorus

Now Jenny was a whore in good old
Cambridge town,

*Who had quickly ****** the Proctor while
he wore his cap and gown;
So his Uncle wrote to Jimmy saying, "Quick
and pack your things,"
For the ******* season opens at the Twelfth
at Kings!"*

Chorus

*His arrival at the University was really quite
grotesque,
For his put his ***** down upon his tutor's
desk,
Said his tutor, "If the bloody thing drops off
at an early date
Please send it. I need it as a special paper
weight."*

Chorus

*Then he went to live with Lilly where he
began to find
That all the other students were queuing up
for a grind,
So underneath the bed he lay despite the
awful smell
So everytime a client came, Young Jimmy
came as well.*

Chorus

*And Lilly's all a farmer's daughter ever
ought to be*

She rubs her Aunt each morning while she has a cup of tea;
He's been through her so many times, the magistrates declare,
That her vagina constitutes a legal thoroughfare.

THE BLACKSMITH TOLD ME BEFORE HE DIED

The blacksmith told me before he died,
And I've no reason to believe he lied,
That no matter how he tried,
His wife was never satisfied.

So he built a bloody great wheel,
Harnessed it to a ***** of steel,
Two balls of brass were filled with cream,
And the whole ***** issue was driven by
steam.

Round and round went the bloody great
wheel,
In and out went the ***** of steel
Till at last the maiden cried:
"Enough, enough, I'm satisfied."

Now we come to the crucial bit:
There was no way of stopping it,
And she was split from **** to ***,
And the whole ******* issue was covered in
****.

RULE BRITANNIA

Rule Britannia, Britannia rules the waves,
*Five Chinese crackers up your ****hole*
Bang, bang, bang, bang, BANG.

MARY'S LAMB

Mary had a little lamb, she also had a bear,
I've often seen our Mary's lamb,
But I've never seen her bare.

RASTUS

I have a dog whose name is Rastus,
Tra la la, tra la la,
I have a dog whose name is Rastus,
Oh ****.
I have a dog whose name is Rastus,
When he farted damn near gassed us.
**** all round the room tra la,
**** all round the room.

I have a dog whose name is Rover
When he **** he **** all over.

I have a dog whose name is Watson
The cheeks of his **** got purple spots on.

I have a dog, a great big Dane,
Wipes his **** and pulls the chain.

*A bus pulled up at a crowded stop, the
conductor bloke looked out,
He rang his bell like bloody hell and I heard
the bastard shout.*

*"Any more for Kew? Any more for Kew?"
A voice came from the waiting queue, "All I
want is a ticket for Kew,
To see the lovely flowers, and smell the lovely
smell."
The conductor said, "All you for Kew, it's that
far queue!"
I said, "For Kew? If I have to get in that far
queue, for Kew, as well!"*

MARIA

Maria, Maria, she's got gonorrhoea,
She gave it to me, amigo,
Oh my amigo,
I will visit the doctor today.

Chorus: Ay yai yai yai,
Si si senora,
Tra la, la la, la la la la la,
Tra la, la la, la la la.

Melinda, Melinda, she pissed from the
window,
She piddled on my sombrero,
on my sombrero,
I will take it to the dry cleaners.

Chorus.

THE WEE WEE SONG

When I was just a wee wee tot,
They put me on my wee wee pot.
There I was to wee wee
Wee wee quite a lot.

Chorus: Wee wee, wee wee, wee wee.

So there I sat on my wee wee pot,
but wee wee I could not,
So they put me in my wee wee cot,
There I wee weed quite a lot.

I LOVE A LASSIE

I love a lassie
She's a great big black Madrasee,
She's as black as the orbs of ******* hell.
Of her **** she makes a parcel
With a file she cleans her ********
With a chota tora pani from the well.

THE SHEIK OF THE LAVATORY

I am the sheik of the lavatory,
                    cha cha cha,
All the pennies belong to me,
                    cha cha cha,
You drop one in ze slot
And then you drop your lot,
I am the man who cleans the brass,
Supplies the paper to wipe your ****,
And everytime you wee wee wee
It's on the sheik of the lavatory,
                    cha cha cha,

BALLS TO BLOODY POCKLINGTON

Balls to bloody Pocklington, Pocklington,
Pocklington,
Balls to bloody Pocklington, dirty old man.
He keeps us waiting while he's masturbating,
So balls to bloody Pocklington, dirty old man.

Contact is undoubtedly the coming game, and the author is confident that these short hints will be useful to all players.

Contact has been revolutionised and improved by the introduction of the Approach Principles and its twin brother the Forcing System. The great thing to remember is that all the usual tricks are used, but the Honour tricks are to be entirely disregarded.

The Forcing Principle:

The Forcing Principle is used to produce Game, and where partner, though possessing game requirements, fails through timidity to disclose them.

Forcing situations occur when:

(1) Partner has great Honour strength and refuses to open.

(2) You possess extra length on a freak.

(3) Partner has a perfect bust and holds no stoppers.

Dont's

(1) Never hold up the game.

(2) Never leave your partner with an unguarded Major.

(3) Never employ the Forcing Principle with a young partner without first considering the results to be obtained by careful manipulation of the hand.

Conventions

The game can sometimes be got underway without ceremony by mentioning a diamond.

The one-over-one is the one of the oldest conventions and still holds good. Partner can signal for a Take-out by making a Squeeze Play (Making a single non-jump take-out so as not to rough Partner's Jack).

The Rule of Eight (a yardstick for determining holdings)

Assuming the Partner has a bare Queen, make an opening in Partner's suit. If Opponent raises, as he probably will, the length of his holding will be revealed. Obviously, your chances of making game with a $4-4\frac{1}{2}$ in. against an opponent with an $8-8\frac{1}{2}$ in. are nil, except perhaps with a dummy set-up.

Leads

Where Partner leads the Queen up to your Jack it is a strong lead. Where Partner holds the Queen in hand after your Jack is exposed, it is a weak lead.

Take-Out

A regulation take-out may be made to prolong the game or to permit Partner to pass. An immediate take-out is essential if partner is vulnerable. A forced take-out is the result of being caught in a minor. A jump take-out is advised when there is danger of losing the rubber.

Re-Entries

Re-entry may be made immediately after a take-out if you have a raise and sufficient strength. Re-entry may be made through your hand provided you know where the Queen lies. Re-entry through your Partner's hand is usually the best expedient, particularly for the novice, but in no case can the entry be guaranteed after the third round.

Suits

In Contact, avoid long suits where possible except in defence play. Short suits are a great advantage and if your partner is void (has no suit at all) better stop. There is no object in raising partner's suit unless you intend to go for game. Never make a Jump Take-Out in a good suit. Many suits have been ruined by this procedure. If partner passes during the opening play it is often necessary to change your suit.

Defensive Play.

The best defensive play is to throw away your Jack. The following plays are considered offensive:

(1) Placing your jack on partner's queen and immediately making a jump.

(2) Cross ruffing. This procedure is difficult of description but in general consists of alternating play with your Jack between partner's Queen and Ace. (You'd be surprised how offensive this is.)

Responses

Normal support is expected from partner, but if partner tries Shut-out, it is better to discard the Jack and open with a Spade.

I was up to my ****hole in turfmold,
At the peat contract down in the bog,
When me slinnie struck something hard sir,
Twas a stick or a stone or a log.

Twas a chest of the finest bog oak sir,
And I wondered just what it might hide,
So I chanced my luck with the fairies,
And took just a wee peep inside.

Now I know that you'll never believe me,
Twas almost too good to be true,
Twas an ancient old Irish French letter,
A relic of Brian Beru.

Yes, an ancient old Irish French letter
Made of elk hide and just one foot tall,
With a wee golden tag at the end sir,
With his name and his stud fees and all.

And I cast my mind back through the ages,
To the days of that hairy old Celt,
Granwaille on the bed lay
And Brian Beru in his pelt.

And I heard him remark rather sternly,
"Now listen we must get this right,
Just as sure as you had your lay last night,
'Tis the hairy side outside tonight."

There once was a man from Newcastle
Who had a collapsible ****hole.
It was handy, you see,
When he farted at tea
He could bend down and make up a parcel.

Chorus: That was a jolly good song,
    Sing us another one do.

There once was a fellow from Kent
Whose **** was so long that it bent.
To save himself trouble
He put it in double.
Instead of coming, he went.

Chorus

There once was a fellow from Reading
Who was constantly wetting the bedding,
Till it made his wife say,
"I don't mind the spray,
It's the stench in the morning I'm dreading."

Chorus

There was a young man from Devizes
Whose ******** were two different sizes.
One weighed a pound
And dragged on the ground
The other was large as a fly's is.

Chorus

There once was a man from Benghazi
Who was having a **** in a carsy.
He was seen by a whore
Who was passing the door,
Who said, "Bravo," and threw in a sprarzy.

Chorus

An insatiable nymph from Penzance
Travelled by bus to south Hants.
Five others ****** her
beside the conductor,
And the driver came twice in his pants.

Chorus

There once was a man from Belgravia,
Found guilty of obscene behaviour.
When he met little girls
He'd rub spunk in their curls
When cautioned he said "Spunk makes 'em
wavier."

Chorus

There was a young ram from Aberystwyth
Who said to a girl he just kissed with,
"That hole in your crutch
Is for ******* and such,
And not just a gadget to **** with."

Chorus

There once was a fellow from Beverley
Who went in for ******* quite heavily.
He ****** night and day
Till his ******** gave way —
but the doctors replaced them quite cleverly.

Chorus

A lady who lived in South Mimms,
Had the most overwhelming of *****.
The priest of the diocese
Had elephantiasis,
So it wasn't all singing and hymns.

Chorus

There once was a lady called Annie,
Who had fleas, lice and crabs up her fanny.
To get up her flue
Was like touring the zoo
There were wild beasts in each nook and
cranny.

Chorus

There was a young lady from Spain,
Who liked a bit now and again,
not now and again,
but now and again,
and again and again and again.

Chorus

A lesbian lass from Khartoum
invited a queer to her room.
As she turned out the light
he said, "Let's get this right.
Who does what and how and to whom?"

Chorus

There was a young fellow from Nottingham
Who saved up tin cans and put snot in 'em
he threw in some ****
to spice it a bit
And sold 'em to small boys who shot in 'em

Chorus

There was a young girl from Baia,
who liked sticking flutes up her rear.
After eating escargots,
she could fart Handel's "Largo"
Her encore was "Ave Maria".

Chorus

There was a young man from Nantucket
Whose **** was so long he could suck it.
As he wiped off his chin
He said with a grin,
"If my ear was a **** I could **** it."

Chorus

There once was a girl from the Cape
Who was raped by a fully-grown ape.

When asked was it horrid,
"All balls and no forehead,
And a ***** like a piece of red tape."

Chorus

Ermyntrude of ample proportions,
always took contraceptive precautions
but one day little Ermyntrude
let a little sperm intrude.
"Does anyone here do abortions?"

Chorus

A policeman from near Clapham Junction
Had a penis which just wouldn't function.
For the rest of his life
He misled his poor wife
With some snot on the end of his truncheon.

Chorus

There once was a bishop from Buckingham
Who wrote "********* and twelve ways of
sucking 'em."
He then went beserk
When outdone by a turk
Who wrote "Women and twelve ways of
******* 'em."

Chorus

There was a young fellow from Stroud
Who could fart unbelievably loud

When he let go a big 'un
Dogs were deafened in Wigan
And the windowpanes splintered in Oudh.

Chorus

There once was a sheik from Algiers,
Why said to his harem, "My dears,
You may think it odd o' me,
But I've given up sodomy
And taken up *******"—loud cheers.

Chorus

Then up spoke his friend the mahout,
"*******'s all very well I've no doubt,
but I just had a bunk
Up an elephant's trunk."
Cries of "Shame", "Dirty Sod", "Chuck 'im
Out."

Chorus

A randy young buck from Lahore
was asked "When do you roger your whore?"
He said "At eleven,
at three, five and seven,
and eight and a quarter past four."

Chorus

There once was a man from St. Paul's
who toured the music halls.
His favourite trick
was to stand on his prick
and roll off the stage on his balls.

Chorus

There once was a girl from Lake Chad
who fancied her father—too bad.
She then caught her brother
going down to her mother,
who said, "Not in the same class as dad".

Chorus

There once was a man from Japan
who couldn't resist a nice fan.
When asked for the reason
he said, "When in season,
I always try to **** as many nice-looking,
sexy, immoral young girls as I possibly can.

Chorus

There was an old monk from Siberia
Who seemed to get wearier and wearier.
No wonder. This monk
kept sharing a bunk
with his girl friend, the Mother Superior.

Chorus

When her daughter got married in Bicester,
Her mother remarked as she kissed her,
"That fellow you've won
is sure to be fun,
Since tea he's ****** me and your sister.

Chorus

To the bishop his girl friend said, "True,
I'm fed up with ******* with you,
I'll take the vicar,
he's longer and thicker,
besides, he comes quicker than you.

The Completely Draining Experience

UP THE CISTERN

A lavish celebration of the smallest room

JAMES RIDDLE

A wind in the ear of all you big spenders, who pass on average at least six days a year closeted away – you can all come out now; you'll never need to feel non-loo again! Relief at last, in this penetrating exploration of tne Great British Obsession. Relax (and discover):

* WHAT happens if you cover the loo-pan with cling film and wait for the unsuspecting user to create a stink
* WHO said 'The evil that men do lives after them'
* IF you're ready to blast off for the executive toilet, or always bogged down on the outside, waiting for life's 'ENGAGED' sign to become 'VACANT'

PLUS

piles of other banal retentions, loophemisms and moving verses

IN

The only book guaranteed to put bums back on seats – and fill every loo in the land!

COMPLETELY EXPURGATED VERSION

NON-FICTION/HUMOUR   0 7221 7350 4   £1.75